Read and Grow with Pepper

Read and Grow

Contents

Pepper is Selfish

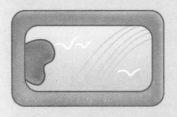

I will draw a beautiful drawing of a mansion. Mommy will be very happy.

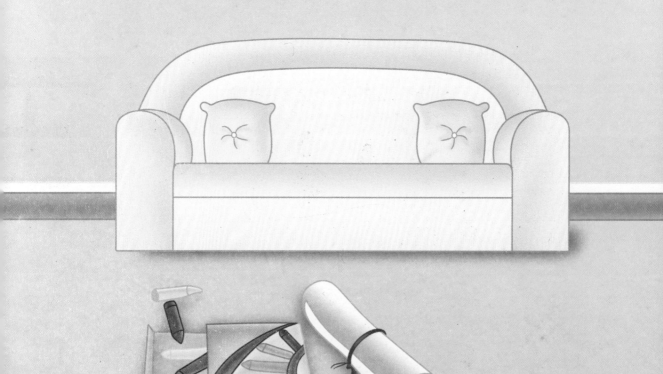

It will have all the colours, red, green, yellow, brown, blue....

I love my crayons.
There are so
many colourful
shades!

These are the best and I will not share them with anyone.

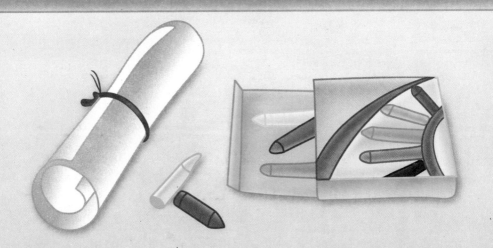

Hello Polly!

Hello Mrs. Brown!

What's wrong?
You seem sad!

I have a drawing test tomorrow and I lost my crayon set.

But...

But Mama, she would have broken all my crayons!

What if you need a certain thing someday and Polly doesn't lend it to you?

Oh Mama! I never thought it that way! I'm sorry!

That's my son!
Go and say sorry to Polly!

Thank you
so much
Pepper!

Mama look!

Very good Pepper!
It looks beautiful.

Now, put it
inside your
bag very
carefully.
Don't
forget.

Now that my painting is done, I can watch television.

I'll keep it in my bag later.

Yayyy!!

Where is my painting?

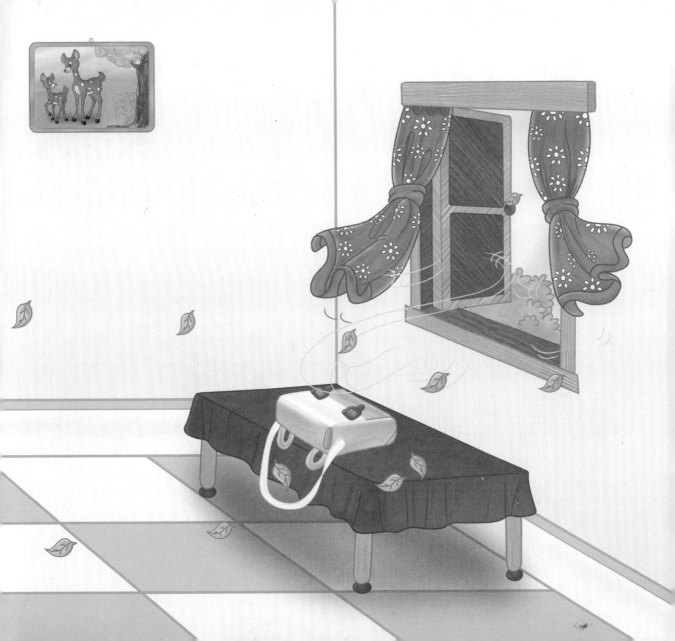

Did I keep it in my bag?

Hmmm... or did I take it to the TV room?

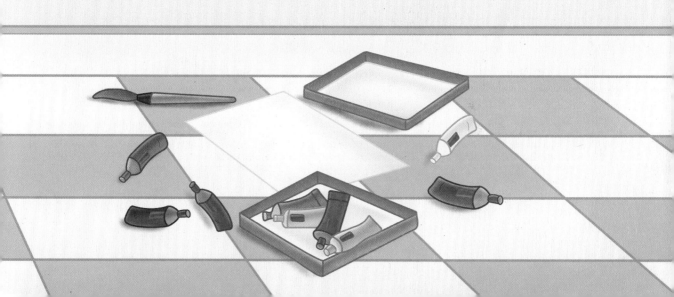

My painting... its not here.

What will I do tomorrow? I worked so hard! Whaaahh!

Didn't you keep it in your bag like I told you to?

Oh! The window is open! The wind must have carried it outside!

Sob! Sob!

Here! Now remember, being careless always brings trouble. First make sure your things are safe. Only then will you find them.

Yes Mama!
I'll remember!

Soon dear!
They will begin
soon.

No, Pepper! You are too young to handle fire. Once you are a little older, you can light as many as you want.

My mother has bought
me a box of firecrackers.
Let's light one. I have a
matchbox too.

Oh come on! It will be fun. We will light only one firecracker! Promise!

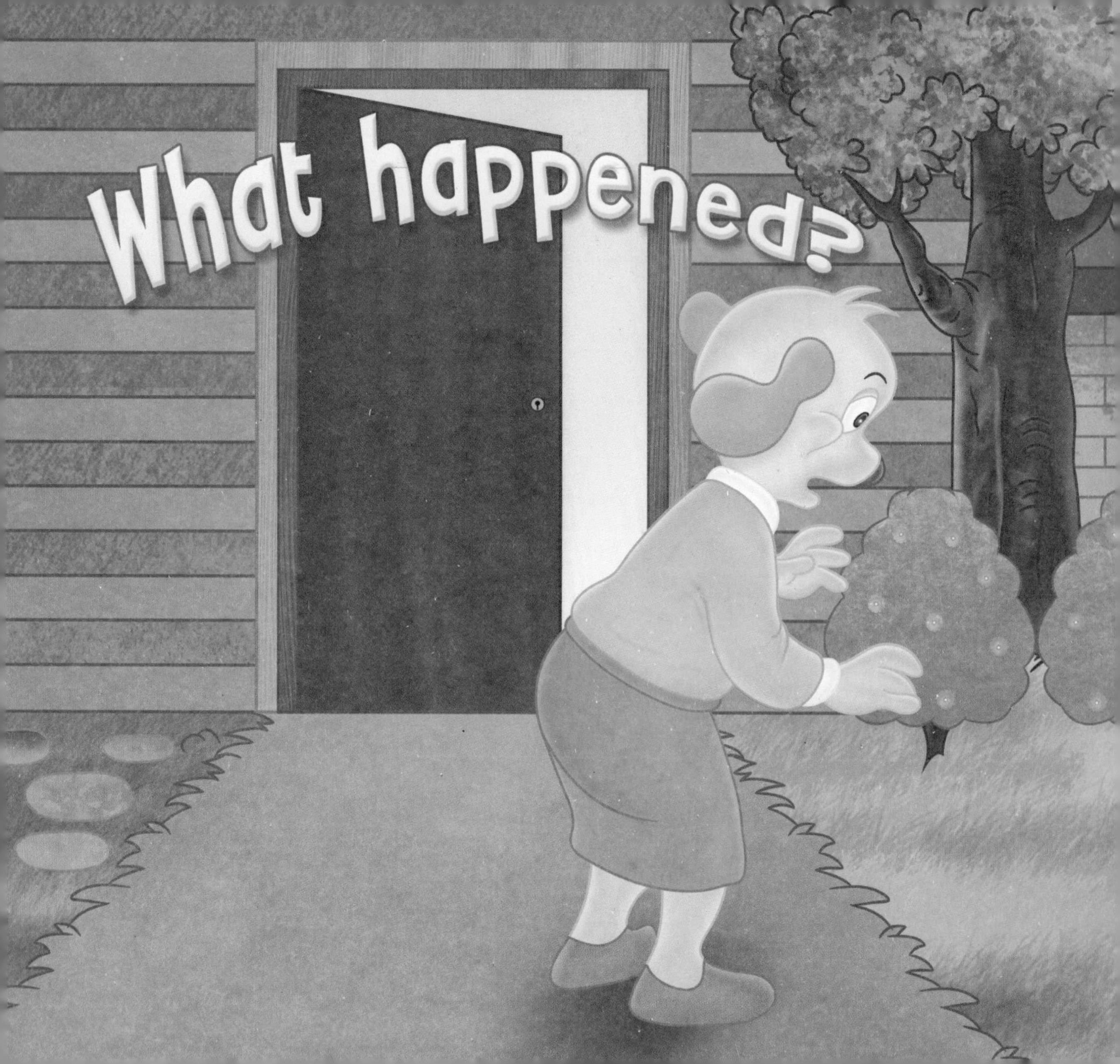
What happened?

We are sorry
Mrs. Brown!
It was my fault!

Now, now! We can light sparklers. But both of you will have to promise that you will keep a safe distance and wear cotton gloves.

We promise!

Pepper Cleans his Room

So many toys!
Which one
should I play
with first?

First I'll play. Then I'll clean!

Let's play with my new toy train!

What are we
playing today?

What happened?
Where's your train?

I can't find it!
I kept it here.

Where have I kept my sports shoes?
Is it under the table?

Oh dear! Didn't I tell you to clean your room?

Sorry! I promise to keep my room tidy from now on.

Let's help Pepper clean his room.

Today is a busy day for Pepper.

His teacher is going to teach him and his classmates how to cross the road.

Yes teacher!

Stop, look, listen and then cross the road! Find a safe place.

Then stop to cross. Next, look to your right and to your left!

Remember children. There are three traffic lights. Red means STOP!

Amber means LOOK!

And when it turns green, it means GO! Always walk on the footpath and use the zebra crossing while crossing the road.

What is the rush? Remember, the teacher said to be careful.

I am so sorry
Ted...

Always remember the road rules while crossing the road. Now, with a broken leg means no football for three weeks.

Children, eating green vegetables is a very good habit!

They make us strong and healthy.
Junk food makes us ill.

But Pepper teacher said not to eat so much junk food!

No Pepper, green vegetables are good for you. You had lots of candies last night!

Pepper, stop throwing tantrums! Don't complaint if your stomach hurts!

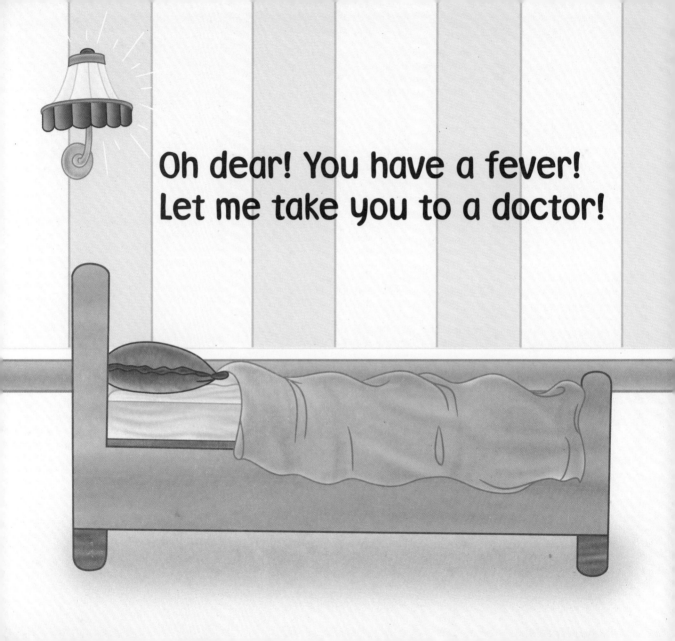

Eating green vegetables will keep you fit and healthy. Junk food will make you sick.

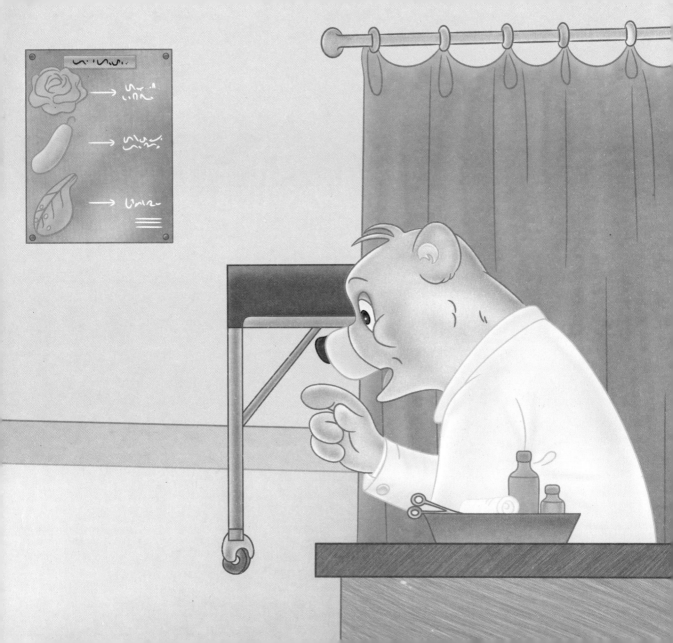

Sorry Doctor!
I will eat green vegetables
even if I don't like them.

Very well said! Eat
healthy, stay fit.

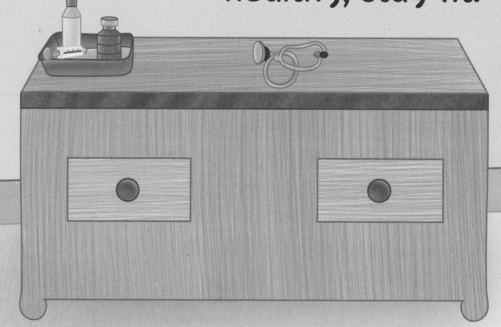